After one of my approached me and famous Belgians, it b̲e̲i̲n̲g̲ ̲a̲ ̲p̲o̲p̲u̲l̲a̲r̲ ̲b̲e̲l̲i̲e̲f̲ ̲t̲h̲a̲t̲ ̲t̲h̲e̲r̲e̲ are no famous Belgians. I managed to do so, albeit two were fictitious – Hercule Poirot and Tintin! The following week I included a question to which the answer was Belgium and it has become my trademark ever since. As you will see from this book, there are in fact a great number of famous Belgians. This is no mean feat considering that although in 50 BC, after the conquest by Julius Caesar during his Gallic Wars, it became one of the three main provinces of Gaul, known as the *Tres Galliae*, and Caesar noted that the Belgae were "the bravest of the three peoples, being farthest removed from the highly developed civilization of the Roman Province, least often visited by merchants with enervating luxuries for sale, and nearest to the Germans across the Rhine, with whom they are continually at war", the modern state of Belgium only came into existence in 1830, after a series of riots inspired by a performance of the French composer Daniel Auber's *La Muette de Portici* at the Brussels opera house of *La Monnaie*.

Published by
David Albury Publishing
Scotland
UK

The moral right of the author has been asserted

ISBN 978-1-9999366-0-0

Set in Times New Roman
Printed by Crawford Print & Design
25 Rodney Street, Edinburgh EH7 4EL

1   What nationality was Adolphe Sax, the inventor of the saxophone?   *Belgian*

2   In which country is the original town of Spa?   *Belgium*

3   Where in Europe are the Headquarters of NATO?   *Belgium*

4   What nationality is Agatha Christie's detective, Hercule Poirot?   *Belgian*

5   The 1956 Eurovision Song Contest was won by Sandra Kim: which country was she representing?   *Belgium*

6   Napoleon was defeated at the Battle of Waterloo: in which country is Waterloo?   *Belgium*

7   What nationality is racing driver Jackie Ickx?   *Belgian*

8   In 1976, during The War of Spanish Succession, the Duke of Marlborough defeated a French army at the Battle of Ramillies: in which country is Ramillies?   *Belgium*

9   What nationality was the singer Jacques Brel?

Belgian

10   From which country does the cyclist Eddie Merckx come?

Belgium

11   What nationality was the playwright Comte Maurice Maeterlinck, who was awarded the Nobel Prize for Literature in 1911?

Belgian

12   Duffel coats are named after the town in which they were originally made: in which country is Duffel?

Belgium

13   What nationality was the painter Pieter Brueghel?

Belgian

14   In which European country is there a province called Luxembourg?

Belgium

15   The runner Emiel Puttemans held the world record for 5,000 metres in 1975: what nationality was he?

Belgian

16   From which country did the artist Rubens come?

Belgium

17   Which country produces Limburger cheese?

Belgium

18 What nationality was the composer Cesar Franck?

Belgian

19 The Duke of Marlborough's army defeated Louis XIV's army at The Battle of Oudenarde in 1708: in which country is Oudenarde? *Belgium*

20 What nationality was the composer Albert Grisar?

Belgian

21 What nationality was the lawyer, Victor de Laveleye, who first suggested the phrase 'V for Victory' in January 1941?

*Belgian: he encouraged the use of the symbol because V stood for both **victoire** ("victory" in French) and **vrijheid** ("freedom" in Dutch)*

22 Of which country did Prince Leopold of Saxe-Coburg become King in 1831? *Belgium*

23 The record for most wins in women's Judo World Championships is held by Ingrid Bergmans: which country did she represent? *Belgium*

24 In which country did the Battle of Ypres take place during World War 1? *Belgium*

25 In which country did the World's Fair take place in 1958? *Belgium*

26   In which country is the Albert Canal?   *Belgium*

27   Which country used to govern Zaire?   *Belgium*

28   In which country were disused mines adopted to contain 500 million cubic metres of gas, making this the world's largest gas-holder?   *Belgium*

29   Which is the only Western country never to have imposed film censorship for adults?   *Belgium*

30   What nationality is Rudy Dehaens, winner of the 1990 World Road Race Championships for Men?   *Belgian*

31   In which country was Thomas More's book 'Utopia' first printed?   *Belgium*

32   What nationality is the jazz guitarist Django Rheinhardt?   *Belgian*

33   Halloysite, a clay-like mineral of hydrated aluminium silicate, is named after the geologist Omalius d'Halloy (1783 - 1875) : what nationality was he?   *Belgian*

34 In which country is Kinepolis, the world's largest cinema complex, with 24 screens and a total seating capacity of 7,000 people? *Belgium*

35 What nationality was the inventor of Bakelite, Lee Hendrik Baekeland? *Belgian*

36 In which country was the actress Audrey Hepburn born? *Belgium*

37 Which country hosted the first international athletics match for women? *Belgium*

38 Which country produced the 1992 Cannes hit film **Man Bites Dog**? *Belgium*

39 What nationality was Word War 1 air ace Willy Coppens? *Belgian*

40 On Saturday October 10th 1992 Phillipe Lejeune became the first non-British competitor to win an international class at the Horse of the Year Show at Wembley: what nationality was he? *Belgian*

41 Which country hosted the 1992 Head Masters Conference? *Belgium*

42 In 1759 a musician, Joseph Merlin, devised a novel way of making an entrance: playing a violin he sailed in on the first example of roller skates: unfortunately, he was unable to stop and crashed into a massive mirror, injuring himself and destroying the violin: what was his nationality? *Belgian*

43 In which country was Ford's replacement for the Sierra, the Mondeo, built? *Belgium*

44 Which was the first country to use dogs officially for police work? *Belgium*

45 What nationality was Jacques Mornard, alias Frank Jacson, who murdered Leon Trotsky in 1940? *Belgian*

46 In which country is Charlotte Brontë's novel 'The Professor' set? *Belgium*

47 In 1994, which country had its police force criticised by the Council of Europe for using excessive violence? *Belgium*

48 Of which country was Leon Degrelle the fascist leader during World War Two? *Belgium*

49 What nationality was composer Albert Grisar? *Belgian*

50 Which country's national football team did Enzo Scifo once captain? *Belgium*

51 In which country was pop star Johnny Hallyday born? *Belgium*

52 What nationality is actor Jean-Claude Van Damme? *Belgian*

53 Against which country did Kenny Dalglish win his first Scottish International cap? *Belgium*

54 What nationality is the film producer Raymond Rouleau, who produced *The Witches of Salem*? *Belgian*

55 What nationality was Luc Jouret, the leader of the cult The Order of the Solar Temple, whose members all died in 1994? *Belgian*

56 What nationality is fashion designer Dries Van Noten? *Belgian*

57 What nationality is footballer Marouane Fellaini, who transferred from Everton to Manchester United in a deal worth £27.5 million in September 2013? *Belgian*

58 What nationality was Willy Claes, who was appointed Secretary General of NATO in 1994?

Belgian

59 Which Formula One Grand Prix did Michael Schumacher win in 1994, but lose on disqualification?

Belgian

60 From which country did Rwanda gain independence in 1962?

Belgium

61 In which country did Dr. John Bull compose the National Anthem 'God Save The King'? *Belgium*

62 What nationality is the only non-British person to have been awarded the Military Cross?

Belgian - his name was Robert Vekemans

63 In which country was the TV series 'Secret Army' set?

Belgium

64 In which country is there a museum of playing cards at Turnhout?

Belgium

65 In which country did the Toc H begin?

Belgium - at Poperinghe

66 What nationality was Paul-Henri Spaak, the first president of the United Nations General Assembly?

Belgian

67 In which country were the 1996 four-in-hand World Championships held? *Belgium*

68 In November 1994 which country hosted the Fred Pringiers Four Nations Hockey Tournament?

Belgium

69 In 1995 calf-carrying ships left Brightlingsea amidst protests: in which country were they unloaded?

Belgium

70 Which country's goalkeeper was voted 'best keeper' at the 1994 World Cup Finals?

Belgium - Michel Preud'homme

71 In 1994, which country designed special coffins to enable horses to be buried standing upright?

Belgium

72 The monarch of which country was the first reigning monarch to be stopped for speeding, in 1900?

Belgium

73 Complete the title of the following classic film: *If It's Tuesday It Must Be ...*? *Belgium*

74   In which country is the largest British War Cemetery in the world?   *Belgium*

75   At the end of 1994, what nationality was the chef that France's Gault-Millau guide book declared 'Cook of the Year'?   *Belgian - Roger Souvereyns*

76   In the TV series 'The Young Indiana Jones', which country's army did Indy join?   *Belgium*

77   In February 1995, which country hosted the meeting of the G7 countries?   *Belgium*

78   In which country was the 1995 European Student Fair held?   *Belgium*

79   What nationality is the artist Jef Geys?   *Belgian*

80   In 1996, what nationality was footballer Armand Benneker, who signed for Dundee United?   *Belgian*

81   What nationality is tennis player Kim Clijsters, a former world No 1 in both singles and doubles?   *Belgian*

82   What nationality is Hippolyte Wouters, who invented Duplicate Scrabble?   *Belgian*

83 In which country was the Sunday Times' writer India
Knight born? *Belgium*

84 Which country hosted the 1995 annual Nudists'
Conference? *Belgium*

85 What nationality was the poet Emile Verhaeren
(1855 - 1916)? *Belgian*

86 In 1995, Marc Degryse was the highest paid
footballer in which country? *Belgium*

87 In which country was the International Gymnastics
Federation founded in 1881? *Belgium*

88 What nationality is film director Jan Bucquoy?
Belgian

89 In 1995, in which country did members of the
National Geographic Institute calculate that the
geographical centre of Europe was located?
Belgium - 4 deg 39 min 59 sec longitutude
and 50 deg 0 min 33 sec latitude,
near the hamlet of Viroinval.

90 What nationality was tennis player Dick Norman,
who, in 1995, knocked the No. 13 seed Stefan
Edberg out of Wimbledon? *Belgian*

91 The open-border policy in Europe is known as the Schengen Group: which country held the presidency of this Group in 1995? *Belgium*

92 Which country hosted the European Amateur Team Championship in golf in 1995? *Belgium*

93 What nationality was the inventor of the bathyscape, Auguste Piccard? *Belgian*

94 In 1995, which country introduced a dating system aimed specifically at motorists, called 'Filedate'? *Belgium*

95 What nationality is tennis player Libor Pimek, who partnered Britain's Clare Wood in Paris in 1995? *Belgian*

96 In which country did golfer Laura Davies win her first championship, in 1985? *Belgium*

97 According to a survey by Eagle Star Insurance Group in 1995, which European country had the most car accidents per 1,000 vehicles? *Belgium*

98 To which country was Group Captain Peter Townsend sent when news of his romance with Princess Margaret was revealed? *Belgium*

99 Which country holds the world famous 'Floralies' every five years?   *Belgium*

100 What nationality is the actress Jacky Lafon?
                                              Belgian

101 In which country was the Vauxhall Cavalier first built, in 1975?   *Belgium*

102 What nationality is footballer Jean-Marc Bosman, who, in 1995, challenged the transfer fee system?
                                              Belgian

103 In which country was the first stamp-dealing establishment established?   *Belgium*

104 What nationality is footballer Vincent Kompany, one-time captain of Manchester City?   *Belgian*

105 What nationality was the founder of structural anthropology, Claude Levi-Strauss?   *Belgian*

106 In 1995, which country did Veronique de Kock represent in the Miss World Contest?   *Belgium*

107 Against which country did Sweden first compete in an International Athletics Match?   *Belgium*

108 In 1995 Elizabeth Taylor acquired a new companion, soap star Walter Geboers: what nationality was he?
Belgian

109 What nationality is tennis player Oliver Rochus, who won the World Junior Tennis Championship in 1995?
Belgian

110 In January 1996 Vice-Admiral Peter Van Dyck died: of which country had he been the Naval Chief of Staff?
Belgium

111 What nationality is darts player Bruno Raes?
Belgian

112 Which country builds the longest rigid single-decker buses?
Belgium

113 What nationality is athlete Peter De Vocht, who won the 1996 Ho Chi Minh City Marathon?
Belgian

114 In 1996, which European country had more than 100 banks, and more branches per head of population than any other country in Europe?
Belgium

115 In 1995, the Prime Minister of which country had paintings seized by bailiffs in payment for one of their client's late tax refund?
Belgium

116 What nationality is tennis player Sabine Appelmans, who won the Gemerali Tournament in Austria in March 1996? *Belgian*

117 In which country did rock singer Alex Harvey die?
Belgium

118 In what country did Sgt. Michael Langley score a record 835 points in ten-pin bowling in 1985?
Belgium

119 Against which country did Paddy Moore Score all four goals to enable Eire to draw back to a 4-4 draw in a 1934 World Cup qualifying Match? *Belgium*

120 In which country are the headquarters of the International Pigeon Fanciers Federation? *Belgium*

121 Stewart Granger's third wife was a Miss World entrant: which country did she represent?
Belgium

122 In which country is the world's highest canal lock elevator? *Belgium*

123 Prince Michael James Alexander Stuart, 7th Count of Albany, lives in Edinburgh and claims to be the rightful King of Scotland: in which country was he born? *Belgium*

124 In which country are the headquarters of the organisation Global Action in the interests of Animals? *Belgium*

125 The monarch of which country abdicated for one day in 1990 in order to allow an Abortion Bill to be passed? *Belgium*

126 In which Grand Prix did Benetton achieve the fastest pit-stop service of 3.23 seconds? *Belgian*

127 Which country has a series of fun parks called 'Sun Parks'? *Belgium*

128 What nationality is fashion designer Olivier Strelli? *Belgian*

129 In 1969 the Queen of which country was turned away from the Vatican because her skirt was deemed to be too short? *Belgium*

130 What nationality are pop group Push? *Belgian*

131 Between 1970 and 1980 inclusive, which country won the Moto-Cross Trophee des Nations 10 times, 9 years successively? *Belgium*

132 What nationality were Frank and Bruno Dumont, who invented land yachting in 1910? *Belgian*

133 What nationality is cyclist Johan Bruyneel, who spectacularly crashed into a ravine during the 1996 Tour de France? *Belgian*

134 In 1996 it was revealed that a new handgun, the five-seveN, had been described as the most powerful handgun in the world: in which country is it manufactured? *Belgium*

135 In the 1996 Olympic Games, what nationality was the first person to set a new World Record?
Belgian - F. Deburghgrave

136 In which country did the Battle of the Bulge take place during World War Two? *Belgium*

137 In 1996 the husband of Princess Stephanie of Monaco was seen - and photographed - in the company of a striptease dancer: what nationality was she?
Belgian

138 What nationality was Oscar Kessel, an archer who holds the world record for taking part in the most World Archery Championships? *Belgian*

139 What nationality is the film producer Jacques Feyder? *Belgian*

140 What nationality is Felix Brasseur, who won the 1996 World four-in-hand horse driving championships? *Belgian*

141 In 1996, which country retired its Royal Yacht, the Avila? *Belgium*

142 In which country is Interbrew, one of the world's largest brewers, based? *Belgium*

143 In 1996, in which country did new adverts for Perrier cause offence because they showed three topless women with Perrier caps over their nipples? *Belgium*

144 In 1996, to which country did Euan Walker, Scotland's No 1 table tennis player at the time, go to play professionally? *Belgium*

145 In which country were shots fired at the Prince of Wales - in 1900? *Belgium*

146 In which country was Baron Victor Horta, a leading exponent of the Art Nouveau Movement, born? *Belgium*

147 Which overseas country's capital city is nearest to London by road? *Belgium*

148 In 1994, what nationality were the winners of the first three places in the Motocross Grand Prix? *Belgian*

149 What nationality is the fashion designer Martin Margiela? *Belgian*

150 In which country are the Galeries Hubert, the earliest covered shopping malls in Europe? *Belgium*

151 In 1995 Stephen Fry walked out of a West End play: to which country did he go? *Belgium*

152 What nationality is tennis player Justine Henin, ranked year-end No. 1 in 2003, 2006 and 2007? *Belgian*

153 What nationality was the winner of the last Equestrian Long Jump to be held in the Olympics, in 1900? *Belgian - Constant van Langendock jumped 6.1 metres on his horse Extra Dry*

154 What nationality is choreographer Anne Teresa de Keersmaeker? *Belgian*

155 In which country is the famous Mannekin Pis statue? *Belgium*

156 What nationality are rock band dEUS? *Belgian*

157 What nationality is footballer Jan Bert Lieve Vertonghen, who signed for Tottenham Hostspur in 2012? *Belgian*

158 What nationality is Alex Lambrecht, who holds the record for the most piercings on his body, with 137? *Belgian*

159 From which country do the Smurfs come? *Belgium*

160 What nationality was Hergé, the creator of Tintin? *Belgian*

161 What nationality is fashion designer Dirk Bikkembergs? *Belgian*

162 In which country did the TV programme 'The Antiques Road Show' find its most valuable discovery, in 1995: a collection of watercolours by a Filipino artist, Jose Honorato Lozano? *Belgium*

163 What nationality was the surrealist artist René Magritte? *Belgian*

164 In which country is the Royal Zoute Golf Course?

Belgium

165 In 1975, in which country was 'The Times' printed for the first time outside the UK? *Belgium*

166 In which country was the DJ Stuart Henry cremated?

Belgium

- it should have been Luxembourg, but when the cortege arrived the crematorium was on fire ! The next nearest crematorium was 100 miles away in Liege.

167 In 1995 The Tall Ships Race started from Leith: in which country did it finish? *Belgium*

168 Which country holds the record for the longest passenger train, with 70 coaches? *Belgium*

169 What nationality was Jules-Jean-Baptiste-Vincent Borde, who was awarded the Nobel Prize for Medicine in 1919? *Belgian*

170 In which country is Mount Botrange the highest point? *Belgium*

171 In which country was the world's longest pastry made? *Belgium - a mille-feuille 3403 feet long*

172 In which country was nurse Edith Cavell arrested in World War One, for helping allied soldiers?

Belgium

173 What nationality was the 1995 World Gut-Barging Champion, Mad Maurice? *Belgian*

174 In which country were the Olympic Oath and the Olympic Flag first used? *Belgium*

175 In which country is Europe's largest ostrich farm?

Belgium

176 In 1996, what nationality was the first European to win the Hawaii Ironman competition, at his first attempt? *Belgian - Luc van Lierde*

177 Which European country has two separate pop music charts? *Belgium - one for French songs and one for Flemish songs*

178 What nationality is former goalkeeper and now TV star Jean-Marie Pfaff? *Belgian*

179 What nationality is Veronique Whitaker, wife of British horse rider Michael? *Belgian*

180 In 1996, of which country was Elio Di Rupo the Deputy Prime Minister? *Belgium*

181 In which country is the Adegem Canadian cemetery?

Belgium

182 In which country was the International Gymnastics Federation founded, in 1881? *Belgium*

183 In which country was Hill 60, which figured in scenes of conflict during World War One? *Belgium*

184 From which country did the first racing pigeons in Britain come? *Belgium - they were a present from the King of Belgium*

185 What nationality is the holder of the record for collecting the most cigarette lighters? *Belgian - Francis Van Herle possessed 58,259 different ones up to June 1996*

186 In which country was the record set for the highest speed attained on the back wheel of a motorbike?

Belgium

187 What nationality was the wife of world speed holder, Donald Campbell? *Belgian - called Tonia, she subsequently married Bill Maynard*

188 In which country was the world record set for the greatest distance covered pushing a pram in 24 hours?

Belgium - set in 1988 at Lede

189 What nationality was cartoonist Andre Franquin, who created Gaston Lagaffe, and died in 1997?

Belgian

190 What nationality is footballer Thibaut Courtois, who made his senior international début in October 2011, becoming the youngest goalkeeper to represent his country?

Belgian

191 What nationality is tennis player Denis Van Uffelen?

Belgian

192 During World War II Robert Maxwell was awarded the MC for storming a pillbox: in which country did he perform this deed?

Belgium

193 In which country are the electronic pop group The Weathermen based?

Belgium

194 What nationality is tennis player Wim Fissette?

Belgian

195 In 1997, in which country did members of the British Serious Fraud Office help the police with investigations into a £100 million fraud following the collapse of the Dai Ichi Kyoto organisation?

Belgium: the head office was based in Brussels

196 In which country is Zaventem airport? *Belgium*

197 What nationality is tennis player Filip Dewulf?
Belgian

198 What nationality is European Women's Judo Champion Ulla Werbrouck? *Belgian*

199 Louis Bonaparte, Prince Napoleon, died on May 3rd 1997: in which country was he born? *Belgium: his mother was Princess Clementine, daughter of King Leopold II*

200 What nationality is Eric De Vlaeminck, holder of the most Cyclo-Cross titles? *Belgian*

201 By 1997, there were only 6 breweries still run by genuine Trappist monks: in which country were 5 of them? *Belgium*

202 What nationality was the first person to reach 100 m.p.h. in a motor car, back in 1904? *Belgian: Louis Rignolly of Ostend*

203 In 1997 Patrick Stevens was the 100 and 200 metre record holder in his country: which country?
Belgium

204 What nationality is Luc van Lierde, who, in 1997, set a new world record for the Ironman Triathlon?

Belgian

205 In which country was a renowned school of campanology founded in 1922 by Jef Denyn?

Belgium

206 What nationality is fashion designer Walter Van Beirendonck?

Belgian

207 In 1997, in which country was world record established for the largest sandcastle to be built?

Belgium

208 What nationality was Etienne Lenoir, who patented the first successful two-stroke gas engine in 1860?

Belgian

209 In which country do people swallow live fish during the annual carnival at Geraadsbergen?　　*Belgium*

210 What nationality are the electronic music group Front 242, whose music featured in the 1992 film *Single White Female*?

Belgian

211 In 1996, in which country did a zoo install solar panels so its two elephants, Dumbo and Dora, could have warm showers? *Belgium*

212 What nationality is sports psychologist Josh Vanstiphout? *Belgian*

213 Fashion designer Hardy Amies was head of the Special Forces mission to which country in 1944? *Belgium*

214 In which country is the Union of International Associations based? *Belgium*

215 In a survey by Olivetti carried out in 1997, which country, along with Britain, was shown to have the highest percentage of households with home computers? *Belgium*

216 What nationality is film director Alain Berliner? *Belgian*

217 What nationality is model Ingrid Seynhaeve? *Belgian*

218 In which country is Eurostat, the European Union's statistics office, based? *Belgium*

219 What nationality is footballer Gilles de Bilde?

Belgian

220 In 1997, which country found that dogs were causing lampposts to fall down because their urine was corroding the metal? *Belgium*

221 Which country was awarded the Olympic football Gold Medal when their opponents walked off the pitch after conceding a second goal?

Belgium - against Czechoslovakia

222 What nationality is footballer Luc Nilis? *Belgian*

223 What nationality is choreographer Wim Vandekeybus?

Belgian

224 Dirk Frimout was the first astronaut from which country? *Belgium*

225 In 1997, of which country was Georges Leekens the national football manager? *Belgium*

226 In 1998 two canoeists set a new record by rowing from Suffolk to which country in 20 hours?

Belgium

227 What nationality was poet Georges Rodenback, who died in Paris in 1898? *Belgian*

228 In which country were Marx and Engels living when they organised the German Workers' Club? *Belgium*

229 In which country did the world's first aerobatic jet team perform? *Belgium, in 1947*

230 What nationality is former world champion cyclist Johan Museeuw? *Belgian*

231 What nationality was the 19th century priest Adolf Daens? *Belgian*

232 In which country are the headquarters of CARTOON, the European Association of Animation Film? *Belgium*

233 What nationality is rally driver Bernard Munster? *Belgian*

234 Which European country has the highest density of street lamps - i.e. the most lamps per kilometre of road? *Belgium*

235 What nationality is footballer Nico van Kerckhoven
Belgian

236 Of which country is Godfried Danneels the Roman
Catholic Cardinal? *Belgium*

237 What nationality is Patrick Sercu, who holds the
record for winning the most 6-day Cyclo-Cross
races? *Belgian*

238 Which country hosted the Eurovision Song Contest
when the UK scored its lowest position, 13th?
Belgium

239 From which country did the 1998 World Subbuteo
champion, Delphine Dieudonne, come? *Belgium*

240 In the final stages of the 1990 World Cup, which
country received the lowest number of yellow cards,
with just 2? *Belgium*

241 What nationality is cyclist Frank Vandenrocke?
Belgian

242 Which country did Melchior Wathelet represent as a
judge on the European Court of Justice? *Belgium*

243 What nationality was the youngest person to win the Eurovision Song contest? *Belgian: Sandra Kim, who won in 1986 aged 13*

244 What nationality is Axelle Red, who sang at the opening ceremony of the 1998 World Cup Finals? *Belgian*

245 Which was the only country to be sent home after the first round of the 1998 World Cup Finals, despite not losing a single game? *Belgium, who drew all three of their games.*

246 What nationality is dressage rider Constantin van Rijckevorsel? *Belgian*

247 In which country did Jim Clark win his first Grand Prix? *Belgium*

248 What nationality is pop group 'K's Choice'? *Belgian*

249 What nationality was architect Henri van de Velde? *Belgian: he was an exponent of Art Nouveau.*

250 In which country is there an official Underpants Museum? *Belgium: founded by film director Jan Bucquoy*

251 What nationality was the author Hendrik Conscience? *Belgian: he wrote the first book published in modern Flemish*

252 What nationality were Nicole and Hugo, who had to withdraw from the 1971 Eurovision Song Contest, but returned in 1973 - and came last? *Belgian*

253 According to a survey in 1998, in which country was the lowest murder rate in Europe - 0.4 deaths per 100,000 population? *Belgium*

254 What nationality is fashion designer Veronique Branquinho? *Belgian*

255 In which country were new, healthy, super-eggs called Columbus developed in 1998? *Belgium*

256 What nationality is fashion designer Olivier Theyskens? *Belgian*

257 In which country did the first motorcycle race take place in which speeds of 100 mph were attained, in 1950? *Belgium*

258 What nationality is M. Mourhit, winner of the 1998 BUPA Great Caledonian 10km run for men?

Belgian

259 From which country does the beer Palm Dobbel come? *Belgium*

260 In 2001, which was the only country with more women than men in the government?   *Belgium*

261 In which country is Virgin Express airlines based?
Belgium

262 What nationality is cyclist Dominique Cornu?
Belgian

263 What nationality was the poet Alice Nahon?
Belgian

264 What nationality was Jef Scherens, the first cyclist to win 6 consecutive world championships (1932-7) in the same event?   *Belgian*

265 In which country is the Brunehaut Brewery?
Belgium

266 What nationality is dramatist Michel de Ghelderode?   *Belgian*

267 In which country did Dame Nellie Melba make her début as an opera singer, on 13 October 1887?   *Belgium, at the Théâtre Royal de la Monnaie in Brussels*

268 What nationality are rock band Soulwax?   *Belgian*

269 What nationality is cyclist Tom Boonen? *Belgian*

270 What nationality is the fashion model Anouck Lepere? *Belgian*

271 What nationality is author Tom Naegels? *Belgian*

272 For which country did Frederick Deburghgrave win its first ever Olympic swimming gold medal?
Belgium

273 What nationality is Raymond Ceulemans, the 1983 world champion at three-cushion billiards? *Belgian*

274 Justine de Jonckheere was the national beauty queen of which country? *Belgium*

275 What nationality is the violinist, conductor and composer Eugene Ysaye? *Belgian*

276 In which country is the yeastless beer faro brewed?
Belgium

277 In which country is the world's largest canal lock?
Belgium – the Kieldrecht Lock in the Port of Antwerp

278 What nationality is painter Jan van Imschoot?
Belgian

279 On which country's racetrack did Ayrton Senna win four consecutive Grand Prix victories, between 1988 and 1991? *Belgium*

280 What nationality is referee Frank De Bleeckere? *Belgian*

281 What nationality is the actor Luk Philips? *Belgian*

282 What nationality is tennis player Steve Darcis? *Belgian*

283 In which country is make-up Artist Daisy Van Winkel based? *Belgium*

284 What nationality is pop musician, vaudeville, professional whistler and Country Music singer Bobbejaan Schoepen? *Belgian*

285 What nationality was Jazz singer and saxophonist Bobby Jaspar? *Belgian*

286 What nationality was the author Camille Lemonnier? *Belgian*

287 What nationality is footballer Stijn Stijnen? *Belgian*

288 To which country did the Duke of Wellington move in 1785? *Belgium*

289 What nationality was violinist Charles Auguste de Bériot?   *Belgian*

290 What nationality was cyclist Firmin Lambot?   *Belgian*

291 What nationality is footballer Thomas Vermaelen   *Belgian*

292 In which country is the world's deepest swimming pool, Nemo 33?   *Belgium*

293 What nationality is tennis player Nancy Feber?   *Belgian*

294 In which country are the Quick Step cycling team based?   *Belgium*

295 What nationality is cyclist Tom Boonen?   *Belgian*

296 What nationality is referee Serge Gumienny?   *Belgian*

297 From which country does the breed of dog known as the Tervuren come?   *Belgium*

298 What nationality was footballer Paul Van Himst, who featured in the 1981 film *Escape to Victory*?   *Belgian*

299 In which country was Olympic champion cyclist Bradley Wiggins born? *Belgium*

300 What nationality is the comedian Gaston Berghmans? *Belgian*

301 What nationality is the athlete Jimmy Verbaeys? *Belgian*

302 In which country is the lingerie company Van de Velde based? *Belgium*

303 What nationality is footballer Eden Hazard? *Belgian*

304 What nationality is Decathlete Hans van Alphen? *Belgian*

305 What nationality is tennis player David Goffin? *Belgian*

306 In which country is the world's only museum of French fries? *Belgium*

307 At the 1900 Olympics, what nationality was the winner of the Live Pigeon shooting? *Belgian*

308 In which country is the Hooge Crater Cemetery? *Belgium*

309 What nationality are heavy metal band Channel Zero?   *Belgian*

310 What nationality is the singer, musician, television presenter and actor Bart August Maria Peeters?
                                                                                              Belgian

311 What nationality was Charles Van Depoele, who invented the electric railway?   *Belgian*

312 In which country did the heaviest defeat in rugby occur?   *Belgium – in 2015*
                                          Soignies lost 356 – 3 to Royal Kituro.
        The referee for the fixture arrived over an hour after
        the scheduled start time and during this period most of
        the Soignies players left as they believed the match had
        been cancelled.

313 What nationality is the model Tom Nuyens, awarded the first Mister World title in 1996?   *Belgian*

314 What nationality was racing driver Jacques Swaters?   *Belgian*

315 In which country is the chemical firm Omega Pharma based?   *Belgium*

316 What nationality is the footballer Kevin Mirallas?
                                                                                              Belgian

317 What nationality is the band Hooverphonic?

Belgian

318 What nationality is Greg van Avermaet, who won the cycling road race gold medal at the 2016 Olympics? *Belgian*

319 What nationality are the band Ian Van Dahl, who had top 10 hits with 'Castles in the Sky' and 'Reason' in 2001 and 2002? *Belgian*

320 What nationality was Jazz singer and saxophonist Bobby Jaspar? *Belgian*

321 What nationality is the artist Pol Bury, born 1922?

Belgian

322 Which Grand Prix did Jim Clark win every year from 1962 to 1965? *Belgian*

323 What nationality is cyclist Andy Cappelle? *Belgian*

324 What nationality is Gaston Roelants, the world's best steeplechaser in the early 1960's and a great cross-country runner? *Belgian*

325 What nationality was architect and designer Victor Horta? *Belgian*

326 Which country did model Brigitta Callens represent at the 1999 Miss World competition? *Belgium*

327 What nationality is actress Els Dottermans? *Belgian*

328 What nationality is Mauro Pawlowski, who started his career as frontman of Evil Superstars in 1992? *Belgian*

329 What nationality was Lucien Van Impe, who won the Tour de France in 1976? *Belgian*

330 Which country did Gaston Salmon represent at the 1912 Stockholm Olympics, competing in three events and winning a gold medal in team épée? *Belgium*

331 What nationality is Ilse Heylen, who won the bronze medal in Judo at the 2004 Athens Summer Olympics? *Belgian*

332 What nationality was the artist Baron James Sidney Ensor? *Belgian*

333 What nationality is jockey Christophe Soumillon, who won The Champion Stakes at Ascot in 2011 and 2016? *Belgian*

334 What nationality was Lucien Van Impe, who won the Tour de France in 1976? *Belgian*

335 What nationality is table-tennis player Jean-Michel Saive? *Belgian*

336 In which country was photographer and art promoter Leon Van Loo born? *Belgium*

337 What nationality is Louis Zimmer, one of the best and most innovative clockmakers in the world? *Belgian*

338 What nationality is boxer Joseph Cornelis, who competed in the 1936 Olympic Games? *Belgian*

339 What nationality is sculptor Jephan de Villiers? *Belgian*

340 What nationality was Dr Evil in the **Austin Powers** films? *Belgian: "My father was a relentless self-improving boulangerie owner from Belgium"*

341 In which country was the 1984 animated film **John the Fearless** produced? *Belgium - it is notable for being the first feature length animated film produced in Flanders in its entirety*

342 What nationality is Paralympic tennis player Els Verhoeven? *Belgian*

343 Which country is the world's largest producer of evergreen Azaleas, with 55 million Azaleas per year? *Belgium*

344 What nationality is tennis player Alison Van Uytvanck? *Belgian*

345 In which country was the luxury car The Minerva manufactured from 1902 until 1938? *Belgium*
- The company became defunct in 1956

346 What nationality is dramatist Michel de Ghelderode? *Belgian*

347 In which country was the peace treaty signed that ended the War of 1812 between the United States and the United Kingdom? *Belgium –*
the Treaty of Ghent, signed on December 24, 1814

348 What nationality was artist Louis van Lint?
Belgian

349 What nationality is diving expert John Nuttyheart?
Belgian